HANDEL

Messiah

1741

a sacred oratorio for soprano, alto, tenor & bass soli,
SATB & orchestra

Edited by Ebenezer Prout

NOVELLO
Borough Green   Sevenoaks   Kent

PREFACE

THE present edition of the vocal score of the " Messiah " agrees in its text with the new edition of the full score which I have prepared at the request of the publishers. Of the need of a revised text I have spoken in detail in the preface to the full score, to which readers are referred ; it will suffice to say here that the older editions are, without one exception, so inaccurate as to give in many places a most incorrect representation of what Handel really intended.

The text here given is founded upon Handel's autograph—now readily accessible through the photo-lithographed facsimiles—and contemporary transcripts by the composer's amanuensis, Christopher Smith. A collation of these sources has necessitated a very large number of changes in the text both of the vocal and instrumental parts. These are fully noted in the preface to the full score ; attention may here be called to a few of the more striking.

In the chorus, " His yoke is easy," Handel's figure—

is incorrectly given—

in all editions nearly every time it occurs. In " Behold the Lamb of God," at bar 16, every edition has in the treble—

Be - hold the Lamb of God,

instead of—

In both cases the autograph is perfectly distinct ; the mistakes were made at first in the earliest published edition (Randall and Abell's, 1767, though known as Walsh's) of the score, and have been copied without hesitation by all subsequent editors. Similar corrections have been necessary in " Lift up your heads." In bars 27 to 29 Handel writes three times—

Who is this King of Glo - ry ?

which appears incorrectly in all editions, thus—

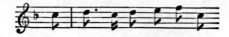

and in the following bars Handel wrote—

The Lord of Hosts

with two quavers (not 𝅘𝅥𝅭 𝅘𝅥𝅮) for the word "of."

A still more important mistake occurs in the bass of bars 69 and 70. All editions have—

whereas Handel wrote—

These examples, which are but a few out of many, will suffice to show the need of a revised and purified text.

In his treatment of the words Handel often follows the Italian method, and when one word ends with a vowel and the next word begins with one, he writes only one note for both syllables, *e.g.*, in No. 4—

And the glo - ry, the glo - ry of the Lord.

Just as we can sing "glorious" as a word of two syllables, it is equally easy to sing "glo-ry of" to two notes; Handel's text is therefore restored here. Similar passages will be found in the "Hallelujah" (alto, bar 24; treble, bar 30; bass, bars 31 and 32) in each of which the last syllable of the word must be sung to the same note as the first syllable of the same word repeated, thus—

Hal - le - lu - jah, Hal - le - lu - jah,

One more instance of the same procedure will be found in the final chorus, where Handel wrote throughout—

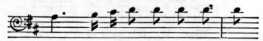

Bless - ing and hon- our, glo-ry and power,

where " -ry and " must be sung as one syllable to the last quaver of the bar, and not to two semiquavers, as given in all earlier editions.

It is well-known to those who have studied the subject that double dots were never, and dotted rests very seldom used in Handel's time, and that consequently the music, if played strictly according to the notation, will in many places not accurately reproduce the composer's intentions. In all such cases I have felt it my duty to give the notes in this edition, not as Handel wrote them, but as he meant them to be played. The full discussion and explanation of these points will be found in the preface to the full score; among the more important examples of this procedure may be instanced the Introduction of the Overture, the recitative, " Thus saith the Lord," and the choruses, " Behold the Lamb of God " and " Surely He hath borne our griefs."

The indications of *piano* and *forte* are for the most part by Handel himself; many of these are wanting in nearly all existing editions. In some cases I have thought it advisable to supplement them, as it is well-known that it was formerly the custom to leave much more to be taught by the conductor at rehearsal than is the case at the present day. For the metronome marks I am responsible; they are not to be necessarily taken as absolutely binding, but only as suggestions of what appears to me to be the suitable *tempo*.

The pianoforte accompaniment is to a great extent new. Of the older arrangements by Dr. Clarke, afterwards Clarke-Whitfeld (1809), and Vincent Novello, but little use could be made, chiefly because they were not so much accompaniments as transcriptions, in which the whole of the voice-parts were included—a method which often necessitated the omission of important features of the orchestration. Besides this, the frequent employment of full chords for the left hand in the lower part of the instrument, common enough in the early part of the last century, is not only contrary to modern usage, but produces a most unpleasant effect.

No attempt has been made to introduce Mozart's contrapuntal additions—*e.g.*, in such movements as " O thou that tellest " or " The people that walked in darkness "—into the accompaniment: first, because it would render it unduly difficult for ordinary use; and secondly, because I have preferred to give Handel's text pure and simple, as far as possible. But I have, of course, filled up the harmony in all cases in which the score contained nothing but a figured bass.

* It is the invariable custom in modern performances to omit a few numbers in the second and third parts of the oratorio. For the sake of completeness these movements are here relegated to an Appendix, in order that the numbers actually performed may follow one another continuously.

London, October, 1902   EBENEZER PROUT

* The numbers formerly included in the appendix have been restored to their original positions, and the paging now agrees with the pocket edition.

December, 1942   NOVELLO AND COMPANY, LIMITED

PART I

PART II

PART III

Nos. 34-36 and 49-52 were formerly printed as an appendix to this edition.—See Preface.

OVERTURE.

No. 1.

No. 2.   RECITATIVE.—COMFORT YE MY PEOPLE.

cry un - to her, that her war - fare, her war - fare is ac- complish'd, that her in - i - qui - ty is par-don'd, that her in - i - qui-ty is par - don'd.

The voice of him that cri-eth in the wil-derness, "Pre-pare ye the way of the Lord, make straight in the des-ert a high-way for our God."

* Handel's MS. has F, the Dublin score D.

No. 3.   **AIR.—EV'RY VALLEY SHALL BE EXALTED.**

Andante. ♩ = 80.

TENOR. A

Ev - 'ry val - ley,   ev - 'ry val - ley..

....shall be ex - alt - ed,   shall be ..... ex - alt - -

-ed, shall be ex - alt - - ed, shall be ex - alt - - - - - - - - - - - - ed, and ev -'ry

moun-tain and hill . . made low, the crook-ed straight,

and the rough places plain, ... the crook-ed

straight, the crook - ed straight, and rough places plain, ...

No. 4.   CHORUS.—AND THE GLORY OF THE LORD.

13

Handel's Messiah.—Novello's Edition.

8332

Handel's Messiah.—Novello's Edition.

8332

No. 5. RECITATIVE.—THUS SAITH THE LORD.

No. 6.   AIR.—BUT WHO MAY ABIDE THE DAY OF HIS COMING?

ner's fire, for He is like a re-

fi - - - - - - - - - - ner's fire,

and who shall stand when He ap - peareth?

F *Larghetto. Tempo 1mo.*

But who may a - bide the day of His com-ing?

and who shall stand, and who shall stand when He ap -

He ap - pear - eth? for He is like a re - fi - ner's fire, and who shall stand when He . . . . . . ap - pear - eth? when He ap - pear - eth? for He is like a re -

STAND

No. 7.   CHORUS.—AND HE SHALL PURIFY.

No. 8.   RECITATIVE.—BEHOLD, A VIRGIN SHALL CONCEIVE.

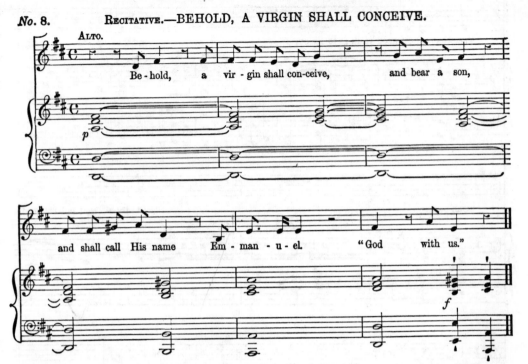

Be - hold, a vir - gin shall con-ceive, and bear a son, and shall call His name Em - man - u - el. "God with us."

No. 9.   AIR AND CHORUS.—O THOU THAT TELLEST GOOD TIDINGS TO ZION.

Andante. ♪ = 138.

6332

thy light is come: and the glo - - - - - - - - ry of the Lord, the glo-ry of the Lord . . . is ris - en, is ris - en up-on . . thee, is ris - en, is ris - en up-on thee, the . . glo-ry, the . . glo-ry, the glo-ry of the Lord . . is ris - en . . up-on thee.

CHORUS.

CRESC(W) —> 47

glo - ry of the Lord ... is ris - en up - on thee.

Lord .... is ris - en up - on thee.

glo - ry of the Lord ... is ris - en up - on thee.

glo - ry of the Lord ... is ris - en up - on thee.

SIT

SIT

SIT

No. 10. RECITATIVE.—FOR BEHOLD, DARKNESS SHALL COVER THE EARTH.

Andante Larghetto. ♩ = 72.

For be-

- hold, dark - ness shall cov - er the earth, and gross dark - ness the

peo - ple, and gross dark - ness the peo - ple: but the Lord shall a-

poco cres.

- rise . . . . up - on thee, and His glo - - -

Handel's Messiah.—Novello's Edition.

8332

No. 11. AIR.—THE PEOPLE THAT WALKED IN DARKNESS.

Larghetto. ♩ = 72.

The peo - ple that walk-ed in dark - - - ness, that walk-ed in dark -

- - ness, the peo - ple that walk - ed, that walk-ed in darkness have

seen a great light, . . a great light, ... have seen a great light:

mf

C

and they that dwell, . . that

p   p

dwell in the land of the shad - - - ow of death, ...

and they that dwell, that dwell in the land, that dwell in the land of the

40

STAND

No. 12.   CHORUS.—FOR UNTO US A CHILD IS BORN.

The Mighty God, The Ev-er-last-ing Fa-ther, The Prince of Peace.

The Mighty God, The Ev-er-last-ing Fa-ther, The Prince of Peace.

The Mighty God, The Ev-er-last-ing Fa-ther, The Prince of Peace. Un-to

The Mighty God, The Ev-er-last-ing Fa-ther, The Prince of Peace.

For un-to us a Child is born,

For un-to

us a Child is born,

For un-to us a Child is born,

un-to

us a Child is born, ... un-to

un-to us a Son is giv-en:

8339

55

No. 18. PASTORAL SYMPHONY.

No. 14. RECITATIVE.—THERE WERE SHEPHERDS ABIDING IN THE FIELD.

RECITATIVE.—AND LO, THE ANGEL OF THE LORD CAME UPON THEM.

No. 15. RECITATIVE.—AND THE ANGEL SAID UNTO THEM.

And the an-gel said un-to them, Fear not; for, be-hold, I bring you good ti-dings of great joy, which shall be to all peo-ple. For un-to you is born this day, in the ci-ty of Da-vid, a Sa-viour, which is Christ the Lord.

No. 16. RECITATIVE.—AND SUDDENLY THERE WAS WITH THE ANGEL.

Allegro. ♩ = 72.

And sud-den-ly there was with the an-gel a mul-ti-tude of the heav'nly host, prais-ing God, and say - ing,

TOWARD

No. 17.

CHORUS.—GLORY TO GOD.

No. 18.   Air.—REJOICE GREATLY, O DAUGHTER OF ZION!

peace un-to the hea - - then, He is . . the right - - eous

Sa - viour, and He shall speak, He shall speak peace, peace, . . .

He shall speak peace . . un - to the hea - - then.

Re-joice, re - joice, re - joice . . . greatly,

re - joice . . . . . .

great-ly,

O daugh - ter of Zi - on! Shout, O daugh-ter of Je -

- ru - sa-lem! Be - hold, thy King com - eth un - to

thee! re - joice, ... re-joice . . .

. . . and shout, shout, shout,

shout, re - joice . . . great-ly,

re - joice . . greatly, O daughter of Zi - on! Shout, . .

. . O daugh-ter of Je - ru - sa-lem! Be-hold, thy King cometh un - to

thee! be-hold thy King com-eth un - to thee!

No. 19. Recitative.—THEN SHALL THE EYES OF THE BLIND BE OPENED.

No. 20. AIR.—HE SHALL FEED HIS FLOCK LIKE A SHEPHERD.

SOPRANO.

Come un - to .. Him, .. all ye that la - bour, come un - to .. Him, ye that are .. hea - vy la - den, and He will give you rest, come un - to .. Him, .. all ye that la - bour, come un - to .. Him, ye that are hea - vy la - den, and He will give you rest. Take His yoke up - on you, and learn .. of Him, for

No. 21.   Chorus.—HIS YOKE IS EASY, AND HIS BURTHEN IS LIGHT.

PART II.

No. 22.   CHORUS.—BEHOLD THE LAMB OF GOD.

No. 23.   AIR.—HE WAS DESPISED.

D

sor-rows, and ac-quaint-ed with grief.

f

FINE.

FINE.

E

Un poco piano.

He gave His back to the smi-ters,

50

He gave His back to the smi-ters, and His cheeks to

them that pluck-ed off the hair, and His cheeks to

them that pluck-ed off the hair, and his cheeks to them that pluck-ed off the

hair : He hid not His face from shame and

spit-ting, He hid not His face from shame, . .

from shame, . . . He hid not His

face from shame, ... from shame and spit-ting.

No. 24.   Chorus.—SURELY HE HATH BORNE OUR GRIEFS.

Segue No. 25.

8332

No. 25. CHORUS.—AND WITH HIS STRIPES WE ARE HEALED.

8332

No. 26.   CHORUS.—ALL WE LIKE SHEEP HAVE GONE ASTRAY.

8332

No. 27. RECITATIVE.—ALL THEY THAT SEE HIM, LAUGH HIM TO SCORN.

TENOR.

All they that see Him, laugh Him to scorn; they shoot out their lips, and shake their heads, say - ing:

Non Legato   *Staccato*

No. 28.   CHORUS.—HE TRUSTED IN GOD THAT HE WOULD DELIVER HIM.

if He de-light in Him, if He de-light . . . .

-light . . . .

if He de-light in Him, if He de-light . . . . .

He trust-ed in God, that He . . would de-

Adagio.

. . . in Him, let Him . . de-liv-er Him, if He de-light in Him.

. . in Him, let Him de-liv-er Him, if He de-light in Him.

. . in Him, let Him, let Him de-liv-er Him, if He de-light in Him.

-liv-er Him, . . let Him, let Him de-liv-er Him, if He de-light in Him.

Adagio.

No. 29.   RECITATIVE.—THY REBUKE HATH BROKEN HIS HEART.

Thy re - buke hath bro - ken His heart; He is full of

heav - i-ness, he is full of heav - i-ness; Thy re- buke hath bro- ken His heart;

He look- ed for some to have pi - ty on Him, but there was no man, neither found He

a - ny to com-fort him; He look- ed for some to have pi - ty on Him,

but there was no man, nei - ther found He a - ny to com - fort Him.

Segue No. 30.

No. 80. AIR.—BEHOLD, AND SEE IF THERE BE ANY SORROW.

No. 81. RECITATIVE.—HE WAS CUT OFF OUT OF THE LAND OF THE LIVING.

No. 82. AIR.—BUT THOU DIDST NOT LEAVE HIS SOUL IN HELL.

No. 88. Chorus.—LIFT UP YOUR HEADS, O YE GATES.

A tempo ordinario. ♩ = 76.

1st Soprano.
Lift up your heads, O ye..gates, and be ye lift up, ye ev-er-last-ing doors, and the

2nd Soprano.
Lift up your heads, O ye..gates, and be ye lift up, ye ev-er-last-ing doors, and the

Alto.
Lift up your heads, O ye..gates, and be ye lift up, ye ev-er-last-ing doors, and the

King of Glo-ry shall come in...

King of Glory shall come in.

King of Glory shall come in...

Tenor.
this Who is the King of Glory? *this* the

Bass.
this Who is the King of Glory? *this* the

* Handel's MS. has " this King," not " the King."

2nd Sop

No. 84. RECITATIVE.—UNTO WHICH OF THE ANGELS SAID HE AT ANY TIME.

Un-to which of the an-gels said He at a-ny time, Thou art My Son, this day have I be-got-ten Thee?

No. 85. CHORUS.—LET ALL THE ANGELS OF GOD WORSHIP HIM.

SOPRANO. Let all the an-gels of God wor - ship Him,

ALTO. Let all the an-gels of God . . wor - ship Him,

TENOR. Let all the an-gels of God wor - ship Him,

BASS. Let all the an-gels of God wor - ship Him,

let all the an - gels of God, let all the an -

let all the an - gels of God wor -

let all the

Handel's Messiah.—Novello's Edition.

No. 36.   Air.—THOU ART GONE UP ON HIGH.

Thou art gone up   on high,   Thou art gone up   on high,

Thou hast led cap-tiv - i - ty   cap - tive, Thou hast led cap-tiv - i - ty

cap - tive, and re - ceiv - - - - - - ed gifts . . for men ;   yea,

God might dwell a - mong them, might dwell . . . .

. . . . a - mong .

them, that the Lord God might dwell a - mong them.

No. 87.   CHORUS.—THE LORD GAVE THE WORD.

No. 38. AIR.—HOW BEAUTIFUL ARE THE FEET.

preach the gos-pel of peace, and bring glad ti - - - dings, and

bring glad ti - - - - dings, glad ti - dings of good things, and

B

bring glad ti - - dings, glad ti-dings of good things, and bring . . . glad ti-dings, glad

ti - dings of good things, glad ti - dings of . . good things!

No. 89. **Chorus.—THEIR SOUND IS GONE OUT INTO ALL LANDS.**

No. 40. Air.—WHY DO THE NATIONS SO FURIOUSLY RAGE TOGETHER.

do the peo - ple im - ag - ine a vain thing? why

do the na - tions rage . . . .

. . . . so fu - rious - ly to -

- ge - ther? why do the peo - ple im -

- ag - - - - - - ine a . . vain

do the na - tions rage . . . .

. . . . so fu - rious-ly to -

- ge - ther, so fu-rious-ly to - ge - ther? and why do the

peo - ple im - ag - ine a vain thing? im -

- ag - - - - ine a vain thing? and

why do the peo - ple im - ag - ine a vain

thing?

Stand

kings of the earth rise up, and the ru - lers take coun - sel to -

Stand

- ge - ther, take coun - - - - - - - - - - - - - - -

The

- - - - - sel,   take   coun - - sel   to -

- ge - ther   against the Lord,   and a - gainst . . . His   a - -

-noint - - - - - - - - - - - - - - - -

- - - - - - - ed,   a-gainst the Lord,   and His a -

-noint - - - - - - - - - - - - - ed.

Segue Chorus, No. 41.

No. 41. CHORUS.—LET US BREAK THEIR BONDS ASUNDER

way their yokes from us, let us break their bonds, and cast a-

way their yokes, . . let us break their bonds, their bonds a - sun - der, and cast a -

way their yokes, let us break their bonds a - sun - der, their bonds a - sun - der, and cast a -

way their yokes from us, let us break their bonds a - sun - der, and cast a -

- way, and cast a - way their yokes from us.

- way, and cast a - way their yokes from us.

- way, and cast a - way their yokes from us.

- way, and cast a - way their yokes from us.

No. 42.   RECITATIVE.—HE THAT DWELLETH IN HEAVEN.

He that dwelleth in heaven shall laugh them to scorn; the Lord shall have them in de-ri-sion.

No. 43.   AIR.—THOU SHALT BREAK THEM.

Andante. ♩ = 84.

Thou shalt break them,   Thou shalt

break them   with a rod .... of i-ron;

poco cres.

No. 44.

CHORUS.—HALLELUJAH!

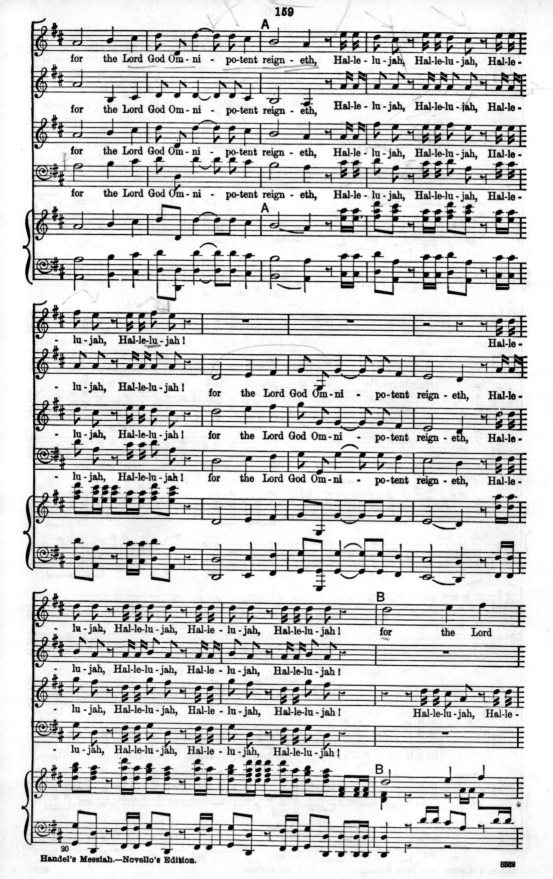

* See Preface.

PART III.

No. 45. **Air.—I KNOW THAT MY REDEEMER LIVETH.**

day . . . . . up-on the earth,

B I know that my Re-deem-er liv-eth, and that

He shall stand . . . . . at the lat - ter day up-on the

C earth, ... up-on the earth, I know . . . that my Re-

-deem-er liv-eth, and He shall stand . . . . at the lat - - ter day

STAND.

CHORUS.—SINCE BY MAN CAME DEATH.

No. 46.

No. 47.   RECITATIVE.—BEHOLD, I TELL YOU A MYSTERY.

Be-hold, I tell you a mys-te-ry; we shall not all sleep, but we shall all be

chang'd in a moment, in the twinkling of an eye, at the last trumpet.

No. 48.   AIR.—THE TRUMPET SHALL SOUND.

Pomposo, ma non Allegro. ♩ = 80.

Trumpet Solo.

and the dead shall be raised, ... be

raised in - cor - rup-ti- ble, be raised in - cor - rup- ti- ble,

and we shall be changed, be changed, ...

and we shall be changed,

and we shall be changed, ... we shall be

* This second part of the Air is generally omitted.

mor - tal must put .. on im-mor - tal

- - i-ty, and this mor-tal must put on im-mor-tal -

- - - i-ty, im-mor-tal - i - ty. The

Dal 𝄋

No. 49. RECITATIVE.—THEN SHALL BE BROUGHT TO PASS.

Then shall be brought to pass the saying that is written, Death is swallow'd up in vic-to-ry.

No. 50. DUET.—O DEATH, WHERE IS THY STING?

O death, O death. where, where is thy sting? O death, where is thy

O grave, O

sting? O grave, where is thy vic-to-ry? O grave,

grave, where, where is thy vic-to-ry? where is thy vic-to-ry? O death,

death, O death, where, where is thy sting? where, O grave, where is thy

where, where is thy sting? where, where is thy sting? O grave, where is thy

N.B.—This Duet is given in the abridged form indicated by Handel in the Dublin score. Compare the
Full Score.

No. 51.   CHORUS.—BUT THANKS BE TO GOD.

our Lord Je - sus Christ,

our Lord Je - sus Christ, Who giv - eth us the

our Lord Je - sus Christ, Who giv - eth us the vic - to-ry, Who

Who giv - eth us the vic - to-ry, the vic - to-ry through

A

Who giv - eth us the vic - to-ry through our Lord Je - sus Christ,

vic - to-ry, Who giv - eth us the vic - to-ry through our Lord Je - sus Christ, but

giv - eth us, Who giv - eth us the vic - to - ry through our Lord Je - sus Christ,

our Lord Je - sus Christ, through our Lord Je - sus Christ,

A

10

but

thanks, but thanks, thanks be .. to God, .. . thanks be to God,

but thanks, but thanks, thanks,

No. 52. AIR.—IF GOD BE FOR US, WHO CAN BE AGAINST US?

who is he that con-demn-eth? who is he that com-demn - - - - - eth?

It is Christ that di - ed, yea ra - ther, that is ris - en a - gain,

Who is at the right hand of God, Who

right hand of God, Who is at the right hand of God, at the right hand of God, Who makes in-ter-ces-sion for us.

Adagio. ad lib. f a tempo.

No. 53. Chorus.—WORTHY IS THE LAMB THAT WAS SLAIN.

THE END

Choral Music
OF THE 16th & 17th CENTURIES

Giovanni Gabrieli

IN ECCLESIIS
motet for soloists, chorus, strings, instruments & organ.
Edited by Denis Stevens

Claudio Monteverdi

BEATUS VIR
for SSATTB chorus, instruments & organ. Edited by John Steele

MAGNIFICAT
for soloists, double choir, organ & orchestra.
Edited by John Steele & Denis Stevens

VESPERS
for soloists, double choir, organ & orchestra.
Edited by Denis Stevens

Giovanni da Palestrina

MISSA PAPAE MARCELLI
for unaccompanied SSATBB chorus. Edited by Otto Goldschmidt

STABAT MATER
motet for unaccompanied double choir. Edited by W. Barclay Squire

Giovanni Rovetta

LAUDATE DOMINUM
for SS(A)A(T)TB chorus, instruments & organ. Edited by John Steele

Alessandro Scarlatti

AUDI FILIA
for SSA solo, SSATB chorus, instruments, string orchestra & organ.
Edited by John Steele

ST CECILIA MASS (1720)
for SSATB soli & chorus, string orchestra & organ.
Edited by John Steele

Heinrich Schütz

THE PASSION
a selection from the 'Four Passions'. ATB soli, chorus & organ

novello

Nov. 21st '03.
3 Soloists